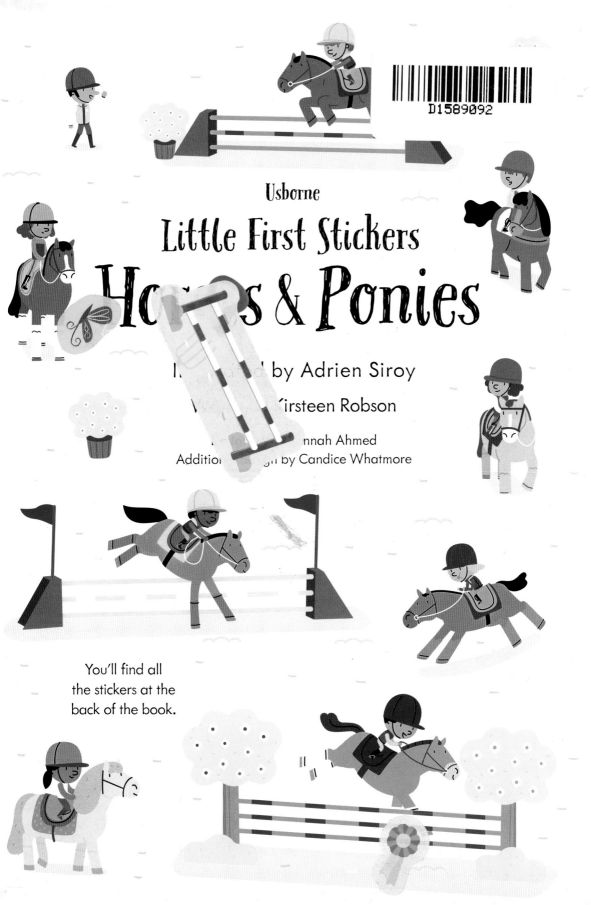

Usborne

Little First Stickers

Horses & Ponies

Illustrated by Adrien Siroy

Written by Kirsteen Robson

Edited by Hannah Ahmed
Additional design by Candice Whatmore

You'll find all
the stickers at the
back of the book.

At the stables

Put a horse in each stall and stick some hay nearby.

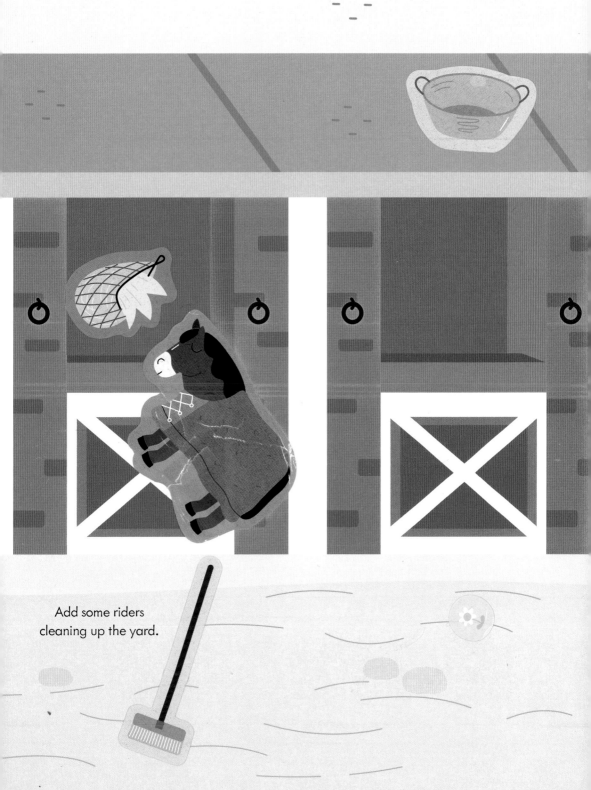

Add some riders
cleaning up the yard.

3

Learning to ride

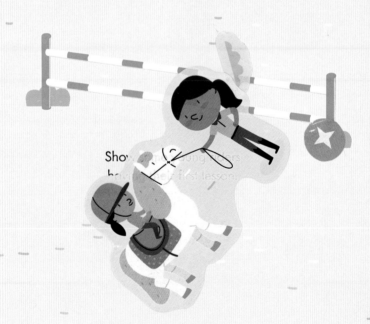

Show two young riders having their first lesson.

Fill the field with flowers
and butterflies.

Competition time

Fill the arena with
competitors performing
their dressage tests.

Position more planters
full of flowers around the
edge of the arena.

New shoes

Stick on some horses and ponies being fitted with new shoes.

Pretty ponies

Decorate the ponies with
bows, ribbons and flowers.

Choose a name sticker
for each pony.

Hungry horses

Show some hungry horses being fed and watered.

Put three horses on the grass to graze.

Pony camp

Position the tents.
Then, arrange some tired
ponies and happy riders
around the campfire.

Sprinkle more stars across the night sky.

Prize winners

Put the proud winners on
the podiums and give them
prize cups and ribbons.

Grand Prix

Learning to ride pages 4-5

In the pasture

pages 6-7

Competition time pages 8-9

New shoes page 10

Pretty ponies page 11

GOLDILOCKS

LUCKY

SANDY

CHESTNUT

Hungry horses pages 12-13

Prize winners page 16